LOOK AND FIND

NICKELODEON™

SpongeBob™
SquarePants

Illustrated by Art Mawhinney
Written by Lynne Roberts

Published by
Louis Weber, C.E.O.
Publications International, Ltd.
7373 North Cicero Avenue
Lincolnwood, Illinois 60712

www.pilbooks.com

Manufactured in China.

8 7 6 5 4 3 2 1

ISBN 0-7853-9837-6

publications international, ltd.

Ahoy, mates! It's springtime in Bikini Bottom. SpongeBob SquarePants needs to do his spring cleaning. If only he could find his springs! When SpongeBob opens his closet to find them, everything crashes down on his spongy head.

Look through the mess for this silly stuff that bonked his brains:

Jellyfish net

Comic books

Sink

Snail food

Spatula

Catcher's mask

Cymbals

Hot sauce

The junk from SpongeBob's closet knocked him silly — or sillier, rather. When he wakes up, he's somewhere that doesn't look like his living room.

"Hoppin' clams! What's going on?" asks the startled sponge.

"You're in Welcome Land!" shouts the crowd. "Welcome!"

While SpongeBob is trying to make some sense of his senses, look around and find these super-happy characters:

Not-Krabby Mr. Krabs

Peppy Patrick

Cheeky Sandy Cheeks

Slaphappy Squidward

Festive flounder

Tickled tuna

Jolly jellyfish

Happy halibut

WELCOME !!!!

WELCOME

YOU'RE ALWAYS WELCOME

WELCOME!

WELCOME

# WELCOME!!!

SpongeBob loves a parade! So when the wacky residents of Welcome Land held a parade just for him, SpongeBob was thrilled to cruise down Main Street on the float of honor. Look around the parade route to find all this seaworthy silliness:

Squid with a scarf

Eel with earmuffs

Carp with a cold

Snail on a scooter

Sausage skates

Baby with a barnacle balloon

Trout in a toupee

Crayfish with a crayon

HEY!

WELCOMELAND JUNK COLLECTORS
LOYAL ORDER of SEA SPONGES

WELCO

ELC

YO!

# WELCOME..

After the parade, the Mayor of Welcome Land escorts SpongeBob home. "Welcome to your new home, SpongeBob! You're always welcome here!"

SpongeBob cannot believe his porous peepers. He has never seen such sandtastic stuff! Look around SpongeBob's new home and see what he sees.

Seahorse carousel

Pickle pinball

Snail racetrack

Taffy trampoline

Spatula sculpture

Krabby patty paint kit

Mud pie playpen

Spaghetti and meatball sundae sandwiches

All of this excitement in Welcome Land has sure given SpongeBob a very unsinkable hunger. He feels like he could eat a giant sea squid and wash it down with a whole platter of Krabby Patties. But the folks at Welcome Land have special treats in store for him.

Look around this seaworthy spread to find these foods SpongeBob can't wait to try:

Peanut and pretzel pizza

Coral kabobs

Tuba sandwich

Tube sock salad

Salmon soupwich

Squid shake

Upside-down sideways cake

Flat tire flapjacks

The friendly Welcome Land folks see that SpongeBob is getting homesick. SpongeBob starts to miss his friends in Bikini Bottom and their favorite things.

The well-meaning characters of Welcome Land bring things to remind SpongeBob of home. Unfortunately, everything is just a little wrong. See if you can find what is wrong before SpongeBob does.

Squidward's trombone

Patrick's shirt

Sandy Cheeks' bio-cube

Gary's fur shampoo

Mr. Krabs' Krabby chicken leg

Plankton's "nice guy" award

Pearl's tutu

Mrs. Puff's boat plane

FINISH

CLEWMOE DNLA

SpongeBob is very homesick for Bikini Bottom. To get back home, he needs to un-bump his head. SpongeBob begins to run in circles—and runs right into a mailbox! Now he is seeing stars and stripes and frogs and toads....

See if you can find this nautical nonsense floating around SpongeBob's head:

Sea horse

Saturn

Donkey

Cuckoo bird

Stars

Spatula

Xylophone

Submarine sandwich

Patrick stops by and finds SpongeBob on the floor. Patrick wheels his porous friend to his place and tries to wake him up, using everything he can think of. Finally, SpongeBob wakes up. Patrick welcomes him home, but SpongeBob doesn't want to hear the word "Welcome" ever again.

Find these things that Patrick used to wake up SpongeBob:

Smelling salts

Noisemaker

Megaphone

Drum

Yipping dog

Horn

Jackhammer

Rooster

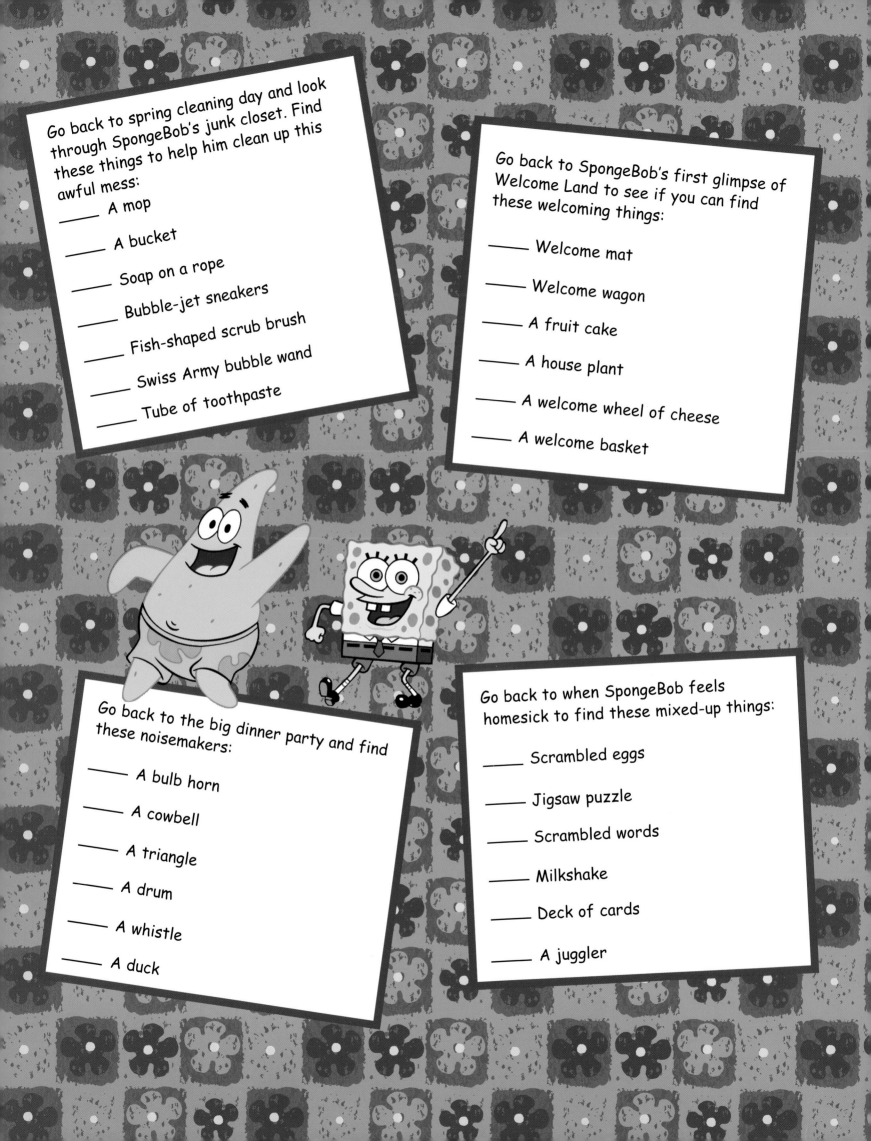

Go back to spring cleaning day and look through SpongeBob's junk closet. Find these things to help him clean up this awful mess:

_____ A mop

_____ A bucket

_____ Soap on a rope

_____ Bubble-jet sneakers

_____ Fish-shaped scrub brush

_____ Swiss Army bubble wand

_____ Tube of toothpaste

Go back to SpongeBob's first glimpse of Welcome Land to see if you can find these welcoming things:

_____ Welcome mat

_____ Welcome wagon

_____ A fruit cake

_____ A house plant

_____ A welcome wheel of cheese

_____ A welcome basket

Go back to the big dinner party and find these noisemakers:

_____ A bulb horn

_____ A cowbell

_____ A triangle

_____ A drum

_____ A whistle

_____ A duck

Go back to when SpongeBob feels homesick to find these mixed-up things:

_____ Scrambled eggs

_____ Jigsaw puzzle

_____ Scrambled words

_____ Milkshake

_____ Deck of cards

_____ A juggler

Go back to the Welcome Land parade to find these yummy treats to munch on while the parade passes:

_____ A porcupine pie

_____ Cotton candy

_____ Caramel apple

_____ Marshmallows on a stick

_____ A seashell salad

_____ A licorice lasso

Go back to SpongeBob's Welcome Land home and find these things that remind him of Bikini Bottom:

_____ A pineapple

_____ A tree dome

_____ Squidward's clarinet

_____ Employee of the month plaque

_____ A can of snail food

_____ A Mermaidman and Barnacleboy comic book

_____ A jellyfishing net

Go back to when SpongeBob's feeling dizzy to find these lumpy things:

_____ A camel

_____ A bowl of oatmeal

_____ A gravy boat

_____ A pillow

_____ A plate of mashed potatoes

_____ An argyle sock

_____ A stack of pancakes

Go back to Patrick's rock house to find these other things that "rock":

_____ Rock star

_____ Rocking chair

_____ A rock and roll

_____ Rock hammer

_____ Rocky Road ice cream

_____ Rocket

_____ Rocking horse